# DIANETICS

## THE MODERN SCIENCE OF MENTAL HEALTH
## EXTENSION COURSE

# L. RON HUBBARD

 PUBLICATIONS, INC.

A DIANETICS® PUBLICATION

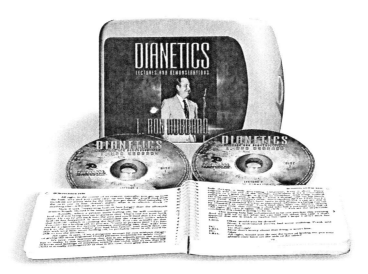

# LESSON NUMBER 1

**Read the *Synopsis, How to Read this Book,* and Book One, Chapter One,
*The Scope of Dianetics.***
**Answer these questions for *The Scope of Dianetics* chapter.**

**Question 1:** Do you agree that Man needs a science of mind? Amplify.

**Question 2:** What would be *your* requirements for a science of the mind?

**Question 3:**   Give what *you* think is the most important part of the scope of Dianetics.

**Read Book One, Chapter Two *The Clear* and answer the following questions.**

**Question 4:**   Describe what *you* would believe an optimum individual would be.

**Question 5:**   Name some tests for the Clear.

**Question 6:**   What are the attributes of Clear?

**Question 7:** What is the relationship between aberrated and unaberrated perceptions?

**Question 8:** Describe *returning*.

**Question 9:** How was the Dianetic term *recall* arrived at?

**Question 10:** What are *imagination* and *creative imagination*?

**Question 11:**   Describe the rationality of Man.




**Question 12:**   Give another example *you* have thought up of a "held-down 7."

- - - - - - - - - - - - - - - - - - - - - - - - - - - - - - - - - - - - - - - - - - - - - - - - -

SUPERVISOR'S GRADE

NAME                                              DATE

ADDRESS

CITY                          STATE        ZIP CODE

PHONE/HOME                    BUSINESS

E-MAIL                                            LESSON NUMBER 1

NAME                                DATE

ADDRESS

CITY                      STATE       ZIP CODE

PHONE/HOME          BUSINESS

E-MAIL                                          GRADE

# LESSON NUMBER 2

**Read Book One, Chapter Three *The Goal of Man* and answer the following questions.**

**Question 13:**    What would be the result of locating the Dynamic Principle of Existence for Man?

**Question 14:**    Where were all factors necessary to the resolution of a science of mind found?

**Question 15:** State the Dynamic Principle of Existence and give any agreement or disagreement you have with this.

**Question 16:** Describe the cyclic aspect and death.

**Question 17:**   Give the relationship between pain and pleasure.

**Question 18:**   Draw from your own lifetime your own survival graph.

**Question 19:**   Give the difference between a *survival dynamic* and a *survival suppressor*.

**Question 20:**   Give the relationship between the scope of the individual and the scope of the species.

**Question 21:** What is meant by mental state on a general, average basis as opposed to the mental state on an acute basis?

**Question 22:** Give an example of your own of the Tone Scale in action for insects.

**Question 23:** Define and give an example of self-determinism.

**Question 24:** Give examples of the pleasure drive.

**Question 25:** Do you agree or disagree with stimulus-response ideas and the pain-drive theory? Explain.

NAME      DATE

ADDRESS

CITY      STATE      ZIP CODE

PHONE/HOME      BUSINESS

E-MAIL      LESSON NUMBER 2

## LESSON NUMBER 3

**Read Book One, Chapter Four *The Four Dynamics* and answer the following questions.**

**Question 26:** Give an example of survival in terms of *self* alone.

**Question 27:** Give an example of survival in terms of the pack alone.

**Question 28:**  Give an example of survival in terms of Mankind.

**Question 29:**  Give an example of survival in terms of sex.

**Question 30:**   Do any of the *dynamics* work independent of the rest of the dynamics? Explain.

**Question 31:**   Relate some experience you have had to the dynamics.

**Question 32:** What is meant by *symbiote*? Give examples.

**Question 33:** Can dynamics be in contest on a rational level?

**Question 34:** What would be an optimum solution? Give four examples from your own experience.

*Student: Do not detach this strip*

SUPERVISOR'S GRADE

NAME                                          DATE

ADDRESS

CITY                        STATE        ZIP CODE

PHONE/HOME              BUSINESS

E-MAIL                                        LESSON NUMBER 3

© 2007 L. Ron Hubbard Library. All Rights Reserved.

# LESSON NUMBER 4

**Read Book One, Chapter Five *Summary* and answer the following questions.**

**Question 35:**   What is the scope of survival?

**Question 36:**   What is meant by the zones of the Tone Scale and why?

**Question 37:** List the *dynamics*.

**Question 38:** What were the first axioms of Dianetics?

**Read Book Two, Chapter One** *The Analytical Mind and the Standard Memory Banks* **and answer the following questions.**

**Question 39:** List the three major divisions of the human mind.

**Question 40:** Describe and give examples in your own words of the analytical mind.

**Question 41:** Describe *percepts*.




**Question 42:** List the powers and responsibilities of the analytical mind.

*Student: Do not detach this strip*

- - - - - - - - - - - - - - - - - - - - - - - - - - - - - - - - - - - - - - - - - - - - - - - - - - - - - - - - -

# LESSON NUMBER 5

**Read Book Two, Chapter Two *The Reactive Mind* and answer the following questions.**

**Question 43:**   How would you have gone about looking for the reactive mind?

**Question 44:**   Give examples of an *engram bank*.

**Question 45:**   Give your ideas of what the source of aberration might be.

**Question 46:**   What is meant in Dianetics by "demons"?

**Question 47:** Describe *pain, painful emotion* and "unconsciousness."

**Question 48:** State the Dianetic version of the single aberrating factor.

**Question 49:** Give some aberrative examples of hypnotism.

**Question 50:** Is there any difference between the *reactive mind bank* and the *engram bank*?

**Question 51:**   What is an *engram*?

**Question 52:**   Cite some examples of engrams from your personal experience.

**Question 53:** What is the difference between a *contra-survival engram* and a *pro-survival engram*?

**Question 54:** What is meant by identification?

**Question 55:** Give another example than that of the fish which might explain an engram.

**Question 56:** What is the Dianetic technical meaning of *restimulator*? And is there any difference between a restimulator and a *key-in*?

**Question 57:** What is meant by a *lock*? Give several examples.

**Question 58:** According to Dianetics, what is the effect of language? Give some examples.

- - - - - - - - - - - - - - - - - - - - - - - - - - - - - - - - - - - - - - - - - - - - - - - -

SUPERVISOR'S GRADE

NAME                                                    DATE

ADDRESS

CITY                          STATE          ZIP CODE

PHONE/HOME                BUSINESS

E-MAIL                                                              LESSON NUMBER 5

## LESSON NUMBER 6

**Read Book Two, Chapter Three *The Cell and the Organism* and answer the following questions.**

**Question 59:**   Which is senior—function or structure?

**Question 60:**   Give a Dianetic reason for analytical shutdown.

**Question 61:**   What is the action of restimulation on an analyzer?

**Question 62:**   Is all restimulation chronic?

**Question 63:** Which has the greatest power of choice – the Clear or the aberree?

**Question 64:** What is meant by *justified thought*? Give an example from your experience.

**Question 65:**   Give an example from your own experience of *dramatization*.

**Question 66:**   What is meant by a *valence*?

**Question 67:** Give some examples of valences from your own experience.

NAME                                    DATE

ADDRESS

CITY                    STATE        ZIP CODE

PHONE/HOME              BUSINESS

E-MAIL

LESSON NUMBER 6

| NAME | | DATE | |
| ADDRESS | | | |
| CITY | STATE | ZIP CODE | |
| PHONE/HOME | BUSINESS | | |
| E-MAIL | | | GRADE |

# LESSON NUMBER 7

**Read Book Two, Chapter Four *The "Demons"* and answer the following questions.**

**Question 68:** What are the yardsticks of Dianetics?

**Question 69:** How does Dianetics regard mysticism and metaphysics? State any disagreement you may have with this.

**Question 70:**   What is demonology?

**Question 71:**   Give a description of *parasitic circuits*. Give an example of how such a circuit might operate.

**Question 72:** What are verbal circuits?

**Question 73:** Does anyone ever use a circuit? Give examples.

**Question 74:** "You" and "I" in circuitry cause what?

**Question 75:** Give examples invented by yourself of literalness of command value in the reactive mind.

SUPERVISOR'S GRADE

NAME                                                    DATE

ADDRESS

CITY                          STATE          ZIP CODE

PHONE/HOME                    BUSINESS

E-MAIL                                                  LESSON NUMBER 7

NAME _____ DATE _____

ADDRESS _____

CITY _____ STATE _____ ZIP CODE _____

PHONE/HOME _____ BUSINESS _____

E-MAIL _____

GRADE

## LESSON NUMBER 8

**Read Book Two, Chapter Five *Psychosomatic Illness* and answer the following questions.**

**Question 76:**   State the non-germ theory of disease.

**Question 77:**   Explain the factors *predisposition*, *precipitation* and *perpetuation*.

**Question 78:**   Define *psychosomatic*.

**Question 79:**   Give an example of how a psychosomatic illness might be generated from an engram.

**Question 80:**   Can engrams be installed?

**Question 81:**   Do engrams have any effects on organic functions? Explain.

**Question 82:**   Do engrams have any effect on the endocrine system?

**Question 83:**   Give the five classes of psychosomatic ills.

**Question 84:** Do engrams have any effect on the receipt of pathology?

**Question 85:** State how psychosomatics may affect the dynamics.

**Question 86:**  Give the law of affinity.




**Question 87:**  What is meant by the Doctrine of the True Datum?

- - - - - - - - - - - - - - - - - - - - - - - - - - - - - - - - - - - - - - - - - - - -

# LESSON NUMBER 9

**Read Book Two, Chapter Six *Emotion and the Dynamics* and answer the following questions.**

**Question 88:**   Are emotion and life force in any way related?

**Question 89:**   Can there be too little emotion? Explain.

**Question 90:** What is meant by *necessity level*? Give an example from your own experience.

**Question 91:** Is the reactive mind above or below Tone 2 on the Survival Chart?

**Question 92:** Give a possible example of your own of a complete cycle of *emotion* down the Tone Scale.

**Question 93:** What is meant by the winning valence? Give examples of your own.

**Question 94:**   Give an example of your own of picking a survival valence.

**Question 95:**   What is meant by personal tone, valence or dramatized tone?

**Question 96:**   What is meant by encysted emotion, life force and theta?

**Question 97:**   Give the engramic evaluation of emotion.

**Question 98:** What is laughter?

*Student: Do not detach this strip*

SUPERVISOR'S GRADE

NAME                                              DATE

ADDRESS

CITY                          STATE        ZIP CODE

PHONE/HOME                    BUSINESS

E-MAIL                                            LESSON NUMBER 9

# Lesson Number 10

**Read Book Two, Chapter Seven *Prenatal Experience and Birth* and answer the following questions.**

**Question 99:**   Give the historical background of prenatal experience.

**Question 100:**   What is meant by narcosynthesis?

**Question 101:** Describe in full the *basic personality* and give your own agreements and disagreements with the possibility of a basic personality existing.

**Question 102:** Trace the discovery of prenatal engrams.

**Question 103:** Does drug hypnotism have any engramic effect?

**Question 104:** Describe "the earlier incident" as a factor in Dianetics.

**Question 105:** What is meant by *basic-basic*? Give an example in your own words.

**Question 106:** Is there such a thing as a non-engramic prenatal recording?

**Question 107:** What is meant by *cellular trace?*

**Question 108:** What did the acceptance of prenatal engrams make possible? Explain.

**Question 109:**  Give the difference between *prenatal engrams* and "prenatal memory."

**Question 110:**  Are there different degrees of aberration susceptibility at different levels of development in the womb?

**Question 111:** Does the reactive mind in any way depend on the analytical mind?

**Question 112:** Could there be any bad effects from attempted abortion?

*Student: Do not detach this strip*

- - - - - - - - - - - - - - - - - - - - - - - - - - - - - - - - - - - - - - - - - - - - - - - - - - - - - - - - -

SUPERVISOR'S GRADE

NAME                                                      DATE

ADDRESS

CITY                                STATE        ZIP CODE

PHONE/HOME                  BUSINESS

E-MAIL

LESSON NUMBER 10

NAME _____  DATE _____

ADDRESS _____

CITY _____  STATE _____  ZIP CODE _____

PHONE/HOME _____  BUSINESS _____

E-MAIL _____  GRADE

# LESSON NUMBER 11

**Read Book Two, Chapter Eight *Contagion of Aberration* and answer the following questions.**

**Question 113:**  What is meant by genetic insanity?

**Question 114:**  Are engrams contagious? How?

**Question 115:** Can an individual in any way alter his pattern of aberration?

**Question 116:** Does a culture influence engram content?

**Question 117:** Give a method of relieving restimulation.

**Question 118:** What is meant by mutually restimulative personnel?

**Question 119:**  What is meant by emotional tone of personnel?

**Question 120:**  What are the social effects of contagion?

**Question 121:** Does war violate any mental law?

**Question 122:** What is the end of the cycle for contagion of aberration in society?

**Question 123:** What is meant by self-determinism in relation to rationality?

**Question 124:** Does Man have an inherent stability?

SUPERVISOR'S GRADE

NAME                                                    DATE

ADDRESS

CITY                          STATE          ZIP CODE

PHONE/HOME                    BUSINESS

E-MAIL                                                  LESSON NUMBER 11

# LESSON NUMBER 12

**Read Book Two, Chapter Nine *Keying-in the Engram* and answer the following questions.**

**Question 125:** How does the reduction of awareness assist a *key-in*?

**Question 126:** Do locks pyramid (build or pile up)?

**Question 127:**   What was meant by conditioning?

**Question 128:**   Can locks be occluded? How?

**Question 129:** What is meant by dwindling spiral?

**Question 130:** Can key-ins be delayed?

**Question 131:** What is the reaction against pain and sources of pain of an individual?

**Question 132:** What are the five ways in which a human being reacts toward a source of danger? List and explain in your own words.

**Question 133:**   When is punishment necessary?

**Question 134:**   Is there any difference of resilience in persons with blocked or unblocked dynamics?

**Question 135:** List valid therapy short of clearing.

**Question 136:** What is the Dianetic attitude toward psychiatry?

- - - - - - - - - - - - - - - - - - - - - - - - - - - - - - - - - - - - - - - - - - - - - - - - - - - -

NAME ............................................................ DATE ............................

ADDRESS ..............................................................................................

CITY ................................ STATE ................ ZIP CODE ..................

PHONE/HOME ........................ BUSINESS ..........................

E-MAIL ..............................................................................................

SUPERVISOR'S GRADE

LESSON NUMBER 12

# LESSON NUMBER 13

**Read Book Two, Chapter Ten *Preventive Dianetics* and answer the following questions.**

**Question 137:** Give the branches of Dianetics.

**Question 138:** Is prevention important?

**Question 139:**   What does fate have to do with prevention?

**Question 140:**   What is meant by accident-prone?

**Question 141:** Is there any way to prevent social aberration?

**Question 142:** Can the individual engram be prevented?

.

**Question 143:** Does childhood illness ever result from engrams?

**Question 144:** Does a mother hold an important role in aberration?

**Question 145:**   What is the importance of silence?

**Question 146:**   Could Man's future be changed by social reforms?

- - - - - - - - - - - - - - - - - - - - - - - - - - - - - - - - - - - - - - - - - - - - - - - - - - - - -

SUPERVISOR'S GRADE

NAME                                                    DATE

ADDRESS

CITY                               STATE          ZIP CODE

PHONE/HOME                    BUSINESS

E-MAIL

LESSON NUMBER 13

# LESSON NUMBER 14

**Read Book Three, Chapter One** *The Mind's Protection* **and answer the following questions.**

**Question 147:** Describe the self-protecting mechanism of the mind.

**Question 148:** Explain why any case is better opened than left closed.

**Read Book Three, Chapter Two** *Release or Clear* **and answer the following questions.**

**Question 149:**   Define *Release*.

**Question 150:**   Compare the value of a Release to that of a Clear and to the contemporary norm.

**Question 151:** What is an *assist*?

**Question 152:** Describe a situation where you could help someone with an assist.

SUPERVISOR'S GRADE

| NAME | | DATE |
| ADDRESS | | |
| CITY | STATE | ZIP CODE |
| PHONE/HOME | BUSINESS | |
| E-MAIL | | |

LESSON NUMBER 14

## LESSON NUMBER 15

**Read Book Three, Chapter Three *The Auditor's Role* and answer the following questions.**

**Question 153:** Define the purpose of Dianetic therapy.

**Question 154:** Explain what happens to the content of the engram bank as engrams are audited out.

**Question 155:** What is the target of the auditor?

**Question 156:** Explain the auditor's role in the session in terms of the preclear, getting the preclear's engrams and getting the preclear to confront and run out his engrams.

**Question 157:**   Give the three levels of healing.

**Question 158:**   Why are the second and third levels of healing unwarranted in Dianetics?

**Question 159:**   What is the Auditor's Code?

**Question 160:**   Give some examples of the Auditor's Code.

SUPERVISOR'S GRADE

NAME

DATE

ADDRESS

CITY                STATE        ZIP CODE

PHONE/HOME            BUSINESS

E-MAIL

LESSON NUMBER 15

# LESSON NUMBER 16

**Read Book Three, Chapter Four *Diagnosis* and answer the following questions.**

**Question 161:** What are the factors the auditor is interested in when diagnosing his preclear?

**Question 162:** What is the importance and use of these factors to the auditor in therapy?

**Read Book Three, Chapter Five** *Returning, the File Clerk and the Time Track* **and answer the following questions.**

**Question 163:** Define *time track* and *file clerk*.

**Question 164:** How does the auditor effect the *return* by addressing the file clerk?

**Question 165:**   What is a *canceller*? Give an example of this.

**Question 166:**   Explain the purpose of the canceller as used by the auditor.

**Question 167:** Do a drawing to show the standard banks, the file clerk, the reactive engram circuits and the portion of the analyzer which is "consciousness" and "I". (As covered on page 248.)

*Student: Do not detach this strip*

- - - - - - - - - - - - - - - - - - - - - - - - - - - - - - - - - - - - - - - - - - - - - - - - - - - - -

SUPERVISOR'S GRADE

NAME                                    DATE

ADDRESS

CITY                    STATE        ZIP CODE

PHONE/HOME              BUSINESS

E-MAIL                                           LESSON NUMBER 16

## LESSON NUMBER 17

**Read Book Three, Chapter Six *The Laws of Returning* and answer the following questions.**

    **Question 168:**   Define *bouncer, holder, denyer, grouper* and *misdirector.*

    **Question 169:**   What effect do these commands have on the analyzer?

**Question 170:** What is *Repeater Technique?*

**Question 171:** Give an example showing the auditor's use of Repeater Technique.

**Question 172:** Give the four techniques available to the auditor.

**Question 173:** How would an auditor use each of these techniques?

| | |
|---|---|
| NAME | DATE |
| ADDRESS | |
| CITY | STATE    ZIP CODE |
| PHONE/HOME | BUSINESS |
| E-MAIL | |

LESSON NUMBER 17

# LESSON NUMBER 18

**Read Book Three, Chapter Seven** *Emotion and the Life Force* **and answer the following questions.**

**Question 174:**   What is meant by push-button?

**Question 175:**   Give your own examples of push-button phrases.

**Question 176:** What is meant by units of life force?

**Question 177:** How does dynamic potential relate to life force?

**Question 178:** Define *associative restimulator.*

**Question 179:** Give an example of an associative restimulator showing how the actual restimulator from an engram has not been identified.

**Question 180:** What is an *ally computation*?

**Question 181:** How does the ally computation relate to survival in the reactive mind?

*Student: Do not detach this strip*

# LESSON NUMBER 19

**Read Book Three, Chapter Eight** *Some Types of Engrams* **and answer the following questions.**

**Question 182:** Give your own example of a phrase which might be found in a sympathy engram.

**Question 183:** Define painful emotion engram. Give an example of one.

**Read Book Three, Chapter Nine: Part One** *Mechanisms and Aspects of Therapy* **and answer the following questions.**

**Question 184:** When entering a case, what are the three case classifications?

**Question 185:** In Dianetic auditing should you be surprised at anything? What should you do?

**Question 186:** Define reduction and erasure.

**Question 187:** What is the function of the somatic strip?

**Question 188:**   What is meant by a *flash answer?*

**Question 189:**   Can flash answers be "demon talk"? Explain.

**Question 190:** What is an engram *chain*?

**Question 191:** Draw an engram chain showing it go down to basic-basic.

# LESSON NUMBER 20

**Read Book Three, Chapter Nine: Part Two *Mechanisms and Aspects of Therapy* and answer the following questions.**

**Question 192:**   What is "tacit consent"?

**Question 193:**   Give your own example showing tacit consent between two people auditing on Dianetics.

**Question 194:** What are the two axioms about mind function with which the auditor must be familiar?

**Question 195:** What does non-optimum behavior of the preclear tell the auditor?

**Question 196:** What is meant by a "Can't believe it" and a "Must believe it" case?

**Question 197:** Give an example showing how these two cases compute.

**Question 198:** Describe the reactive mind's computation of the ally versus the antagonist.

**Question 199:** Explain "auto-control" and why the auditor is necessary to the success of any session.

**Question 200:**   In what two ways is Dianetics first aid useful?

**Question 201:**   What is meant by auditor evaluation?

**Question 202:** In Dianetics, what does auditing mean?

**Question 203:** List some of the Dianetic Don'ts and why they should be applied.

**Question 204:** What must the auditor keep on doing to attain a Release or Clear?

*Student: Do not detach this strip*

| NAME | | DATE |
|------|--|------|
| ADDRESS | | |
| CITY | STATE | ZIP CODE |
| PHONE/HOME | BUSINESS | |
| E-MAIL | | |

LESSON NUMBER 20

## LESSON NUMBER 21

**Read Book Three, Chapter Ten *Dianetics – Past and Future* and answer the following questions.**

**Question 205:**   Define Judiciary Dianetics.

**Question 206:**   What is the fundamental test of rationality? How does this relate to a structure of law or judgment?

**Question 207:**   In what society can Man be truly responsible for his acts?

**Question 208:**   What are the precision definitions for each social level as related to the Tone Scale?

**Question 209:** Is there any national problem that cannot be solved by reason alone? Give your reasons why.

NAME                                    DATE

ADDRESS

CITY                    STATE        ZIP CODE

PHONE/HOME              BUSINESS

E-MAIL

LESSON NUMBER 21

# THETA + MEST

(LIFE FORCE)     (MATTER, ENERGY, SPACE & TIME)

# = LIFE

Dianetics revealed the previously unknown mind that enslaves Man–the *reactive mind*–and the procedures to get rid of it. And what that, in turn, revealed was something far greater–*Life Force* itself. Here are the discoveries of how *theta* interacts with the physical universe of matter, energy, space and time–*MEST*. And what that provides is the route to ascend to higher states–something never envisioned in history. The book is written around the now legendary *Chart of Human Evaluation*, providing a complete description of the Tone Scale and the components of emotion–the "triangle" of Affinity, Reality and Communication. By knowing just one or two characteristics of a person, you can know the rest–their entire personality, conduct and character. Here, then, is not only the essential handbook for every auditor, but for use in life itself. And that's why *Science of Survival* is the most useful book you'll ever own.

DO THE

## Science of Survival Extension Course

AND LISTEN TO

## The Science of Survival Lectures

YES, I WANT TO ENROLL ON THE SCIENCE OF SURVIVAL EXTENSION COURSE
AND ORDER THE SCIENCE OF SURVIVAL LECTURES

NAME

ADDRESS

CITY        STATE/PROVINCE        POSTAL CODE

COUNTRY        TELEPHONE

E-MAIL